The Swapping Boy

Home Sweet Home

JOHN LANGSTAFF

THE SWAPPING BOY

With pictures by

Beth and Joe Krush

HARCOURT, BRACE AND COMPANY
NEW YORK

*Dedicated to the musician, Cecil Sharp, born one hundred years ago,
whose great collecting and understanding of the folk songs he
loved have given such enjoyment to me and to many boys
and girls who have learned the songs from his books*

 First edition.
Library of Congress Catalog Card Number: 60-11251
Printed in the United States of America

This swapping song about the foolish boy is one of our folk songs that belongs especially to boys and girls. The beginnings of this song are five hundred years old, going back to a time in England before books were printed, and when, instead of learning to sing songs from books, children just learned them from their fathers and mothers. As with all of our folk songs, there are lots of versions of this story. I have chosen those words that I like best from different parts of our country. Of the many "Swapping Song" tunes we could use for this book, I've taken my favorite—one that we used to sing in my family when I was a little boy. This tune was discovered by Cecil Sharp, an Englishman who came to our country forty years ago to help us find our folk music in the Southern Appalachian Mountains. In those days, he had to walk or go by horse up the steep hills and down the narrow valleys, along the dry creek beds and rough mountain trails, to find the friendly people who remembered the old songs. He sat with them on the porches of their cabins and in front of their fires, listening to these songs and writing them down for other people to learn and enjoy. Some of the best songs Mr. Sharp found were sung to him by children. These are *our* songs, yours and mine, and his.

J. L.

When I was a little boy, I lived by myself,
And all the bread and cheese I had I kept upon the shelf.

To my wing wong waddle, to my Jack straw straddle,
to my Johnny's got his fiddle, and he's gone on home.

The rats and the mice they led me such a life,
I had to go to London to get me a wife.

To my wing wong waddle, to my Jack straw straddle,
to my Johnny's got his fiddle, and he's gone on home.

The creeks were so wide and the lanes were so narrow,
I had to bring her home in an old wheelbarrow.

To my wing wong waddle, to my Jack straw straddle,
to my Johnny's got his fiddle, and he's gone on home.

STONEWALLS
Feed Seed

My foot it slipped and I got a fall,
And down came my wheelbarrow, wife and all!

To my wing wong waddle, to my Jack straw straddle,
to my Johnny's got his fiddle, and he's gone on home.

I swapped my wheelbarrow and got me a mare,
And then I rode from fair to fair.

To my wing wong waddle, to my Jack straw straddle,
to my Johnny's got his fiddle, and he's gone on home.

I swapped my mare and got me a cow,
But then to milk her, I didn't know how.

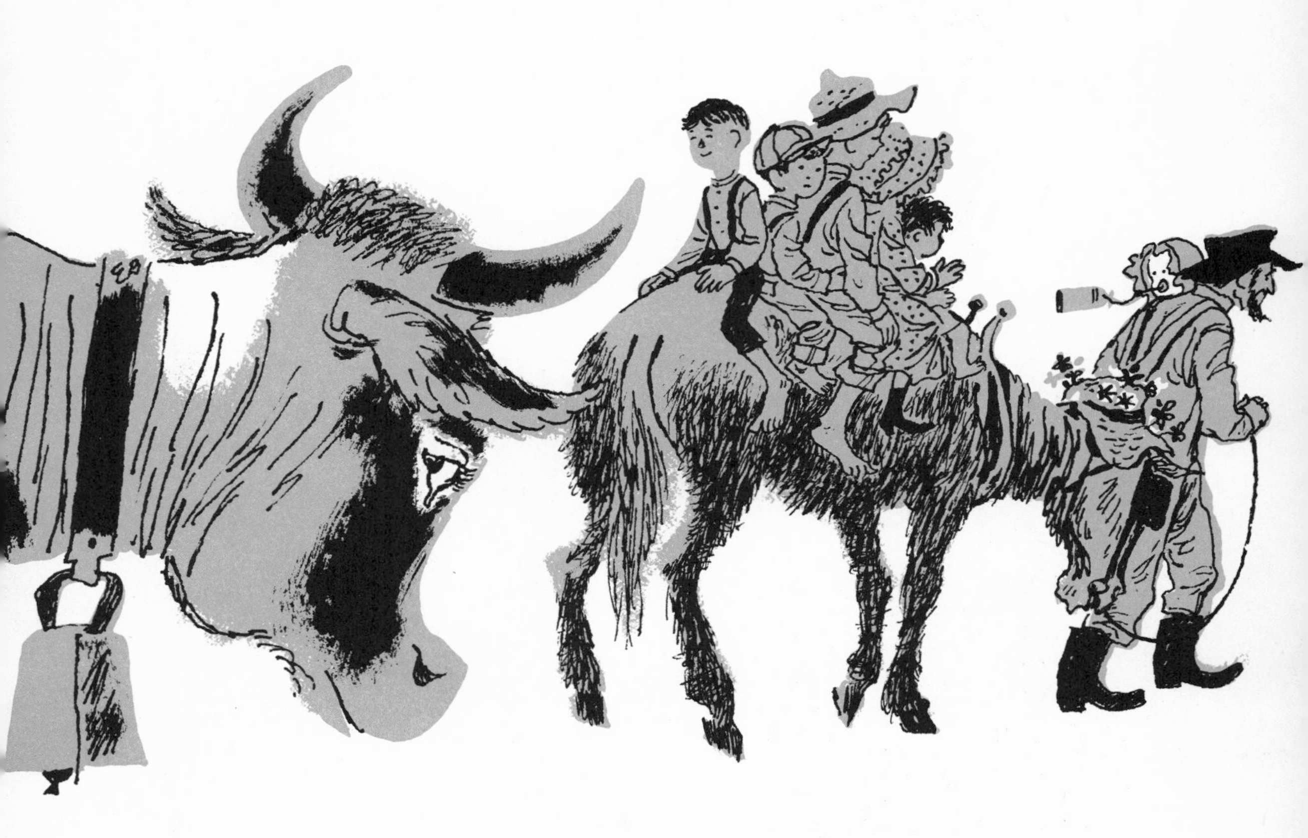

To my wing wong waddle, to my Jack straw straddle,
to my Johnny's got his fiddle, and he's gone on home.

I swapped my cow and got me a calf,
And in that trade I just lost half.

To my wing wong waddle, to my Jack straw straddle,
to my Johnny's got his fiddle, and he's gone on home.

I swapped my calf and got me a mule,
And then I rode like a doggone fool!

To my wing wong waddle, to my Jack straw straddle,
to my Johnny's got his fiddle, and he's gone on home.

I swapped my mule and got me a sheep,
And then I rode till I went to sleep.

To my wing wong waddle, to my Jack straw straddle,
to my Johnny's got his fiddle, and he's gone on home.

I swapped my sheep and got me a goat,
But when I got him, he would not tote.

To my wing wong waddle, to my Jack straw straddle,
to my Johnny's got his fiddle, and he's gone on home.

I swapped my goat and got me a pig,
The poor little thing it never grew big.

To my wing wong waddle, to my Jack straw straddle,
to my Johnny's got his fiddle, and he's gone on home.

I swapped my pig and got me a hen,
Oh, what a pretty thing I had then!

To my wing wong waddle, to my Jack straw straddle,
to my Johnny's got his fiddle, and he's gone on home.

I swapped my hen and got me a cat,
When she went to sleep, she slept in my hat.

To my wing wong waddle, to my Jack straw straddle,
to my Johnny's got his fiddle, and he's gone on home.

I swapped my cat and got me a mole,
And the durn'd old thing went straight to its hole.

To my wing wong waddle, to my Jack straw straddle,
to my Johnny's got his fiddle, and he's gone on home.

And now the songbook's back on the shelf,
If you want any more, you can sing it yourself!

To my wing wong waddle, to my Jack straw straddle,
to my Johnny's got his fiddle, and he's gone on home.

The Swapping Song

From *Nursery Songs from the Appalachian Mountains*
collected and arranged by Cecil J. Sharp